First published in Great Britain 2022 by Farshore
An imprint of HarperCollins*Publishers*
1 London Bridge Street, London SE1 9GF
www.farshore.co.uk

HarperCollins*Publishers*
1st Floor, Watermarque Building, Ringsend Road
Dublin 4, Ireland

ISBN 978 0 0085 0765 7
Printed in Romania
001

Written by Emily Stead.

A CIP catalogue record for this book is available from the British Library.

Parental guidance is advised for all craft and colouring activities. Always ask an adult to help when using glue,
paint and scissors. Wear protective clothing and cover surfaces to avoid staining.

Stay safe online. Farshore is not responsible for content hosted by third parties.

Images used under license from Shutterstock.com

MIX
Paper from
responsible sources
FSC™ C007454

FSC
www.fsc.org

This book is produced from independently certified FSC™ paper
to ensure responsible forest management.

For more information visit: www.harpercollins.co.uk/green

ANNUAL 2023

THIS BOOK BELONGS TO:

....

....

Contents

Welcome to Adventure Bay

EVEREST

CHASE

SKYE

RYDER

ROCKY

MARSHALL

RUBBLE

ZUMA

... where Ryder and the PAW Patrol are ready to race to the rescue and save anyone in trouble. This book is packed with puzzles, activities and stories, featuring all your favourite pups! So remember, whenever you need them, just yelp for help!

Ready for Action!

Ryder and the PAW Patrol are always ready for any job, big or small! Tick the boxes as you find Ryder and the pups in the picture.

8

The answers are on page 69.

Clever CHASE

Police pup Chase can always sniff out danger! Copy the little picture to colour him in.

Pup Fact

Feathers and cats make poor Chase sneeze!

On the CASE!

Are you good at spotting things like Chase? Look closely at the shadows – which one matches the picture of Chase?

a

b

c

d

The answer is on page 69.

Beach BUDDIES

Join the dots to reveal something that will help Skye and Rubble to stay safe in the sun.

12

Perfect PETS

There's been a mix-up in Adventure Bay! Follow the lines to help these people find their pets. One person doesn't have a pet – do you know who?

Farmer Yumi

Katie

Ryder

Mayor Goodway

Chickaletta

Bettina

Cali

The answers are on page 69.

Pups Save a Super Pup

1

The pups were watching one of their favourite cartoons on TV. "I love *Apollo the Super Pup*!" said Rubble.

2

Any pup want a game?

Just then, Ryder appeared. "Who wants to play football? Rubble?" he asked. "No thanks!" said Rubble. "I'm going to play *Rubble the Super Pup* and save the day my own way!"

3

"Who can I save?" thought Rubble. "Farmer Yumi might need some help around the farm," Ryder replied. "Great idea!" said Rubble. He rushed out of the Lookout to the farm.

4

I need your help!

CLUCK!

CLUCK!

"My chickens have flown the coop!" said Farmer Yumi. "Can you help?" Rubble herded the chickens safely back into their coop. "Super Pup saves the day!" he cried.

5 Rubble wanted to know what else he could do to save the day. "Mayor Goodway might need some help!" said Farmer Yumi.

Go and see Mayor Goodway!

6 We need the PAW Patrol!

7

"Rubble!" cried Mayor Goodway. "The train driver called to say there's been a rockslide – his train is stuck in a tunnel! Call Ryder and the PAW Patrol!" But Rubble decided he could save the day on his own.

Rubble tried to move the rocks by himself. He pushed a boulder as hard as he could, but more rocks fell, blocking the tunnel. Rubble, the train driver and the train were all trapped! "Oops!" said Rubble.

Will we ever get out of here?

I'm calling the PAW Patrol!

"I'm sorry!" said Rubble. "I thought I could do it myself. I didn't save the day, I just made everything worse!"

Rubble used his Pup Tag to call Ryder. "I need the PAW Patrol on the double!" he said. "We're on our way!" said Ryder.

10 Ryder, Zuma and Chase arrived at the tunnel. Zuma was driving Rubble's rig. "Chase, see if you can make Rubble an exit!" said Ryder. Chase used his winch to make a small hole.

I've got this, don't worry!

11

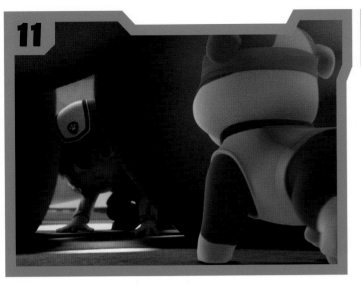

Chase moved the bigger rocks out of the way, then Zuma drove Rubble's rig to move more rocks, so Rubble could squeeze out. "Thanks!" said Rubble.

12

Next, Rubble cleared the last few rocks, so the train driver could drive safely out of the tunnel. "Rubble, you did it!" said the driver. "You saved the day!"

13

Hurray, we are free!

"You mean, I helped save the day the PAW Patrol way!" said Rubble. "You're right!" said the driver. "Thanks Ryder, and you too, pups."

14

Come on pups, let's play!

Back at the Lookout it was time for some fun. "Who wants to play catch?" asked Rocky. "Let's all play together, the PAW Patrol way!" smiled Rubble.

Well done, pups!

Here Comes RUBBLE!

What is busy Rubble carrying in his shovel today? Draw it in, then colour in the picture.

Pup Fact

Rubble never minds getting dirty as he loves bubble baths!

Take a BREAK

Now it's time for some fun in the sun! Find the two pictures of Rubble in his rubber ring that are exactly the same.

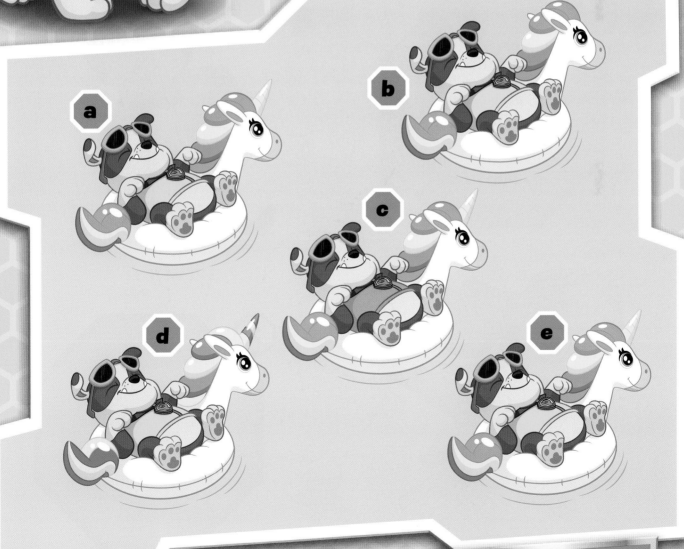

a

b

c

d

e

The answers are on page 69.

Guess WHO?

Ryder is playing a game with the pups. Read the clues, then draw a line to match each pup with their description.

1

a. I love to do backflips!

b. Pink is my favourite colour.

c. I can fly using my Pup Pack.

2

a. My eyes are brown.

b. Cats make me sneeze! Achoo!

c. I'm a German Shepherd pup.

3

a. My eyes are blue.

b. Ice or snow, I'm ready to go!

c. I'm a helpful Husky pup.

4

a. My eyes are brown.

b. I just love skateboarding!

c. I get there on the double!

5

a. My eyes are brown.

b. My fur is grey.

c. I'm great at recycling and fixing things.

6

a. I love to make a splash!

b. My badge shows a picture of an anchor.

c. My fur is the colour of chocolate!

The answers are on page 69.

21

Smart SKYE!

Skye is a daredevil pilot pup! Colour her in using your brightest pens.

Pup Fact

When Skye's not in the air, she loves riding the slopes on her snowboard!

This Pup's Gotta FLY!

These friends all have wings, just like Skye! But only one can't fly. Can you work out which one and circle it?

bee

butterfly

seagull

penguin

owl

The answer is on page 69.

Party PUPS!

Ryder and the pups love to party!

1

Can you spot six differences in picture 2?

Colour in a balloon for each difference that you find.

The answers are on page 69.

25

On the ROAD

Chase has been chosen for an important job! Can you help him collect all the cones on his way to reach Ryder? Tick each cone that Chase finds.

Start

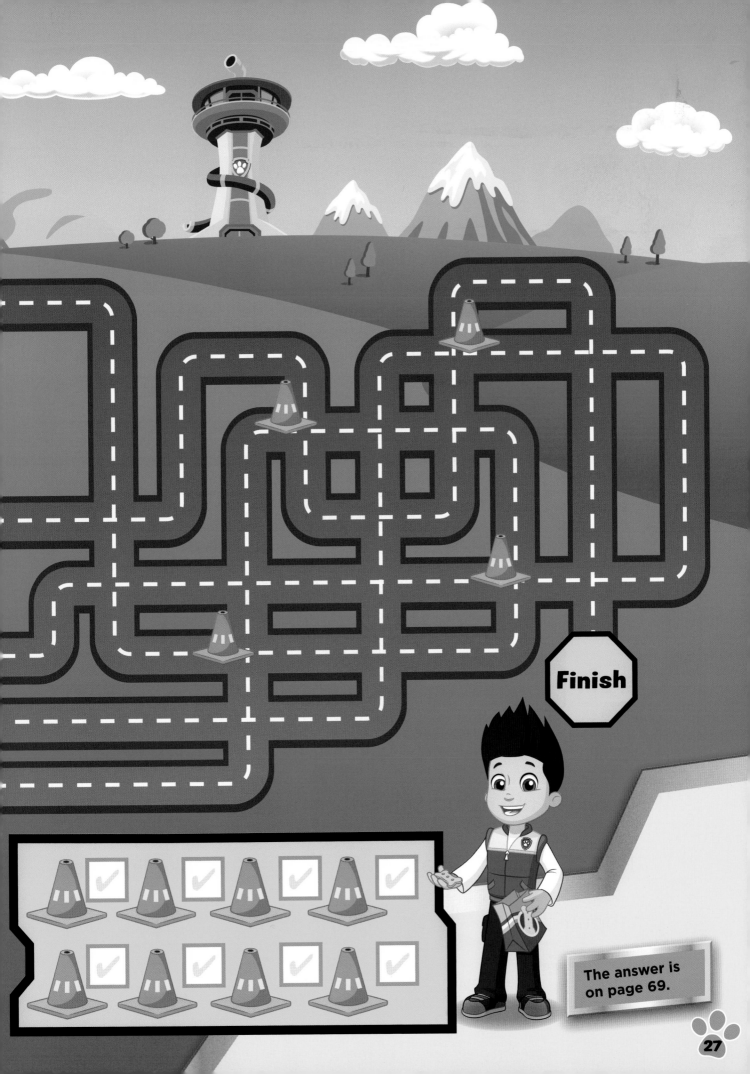

Finish

The answer is on page 69.

Pups Get a Lift

Read along with the story. Each time you get to a picture, say the name out loud.

Key:

Ryder Marshall Katie Cali Rubble

 and the pups were at the Lookout playing football when there was a call on 's PupPad. It was Jake calling. "The mountain chair lift has broken!" he told . "Most people are safe, but and are stranded!"

 quickly gathered the pups – it was a job for the PAW Patrol! On the mountain, tried to drive his fire truck down the slope, but the path was too icy. "Tell Jake I'm fine!" shouted. "But is getting cold up here."

Clever knew what to do, and called to help.

While 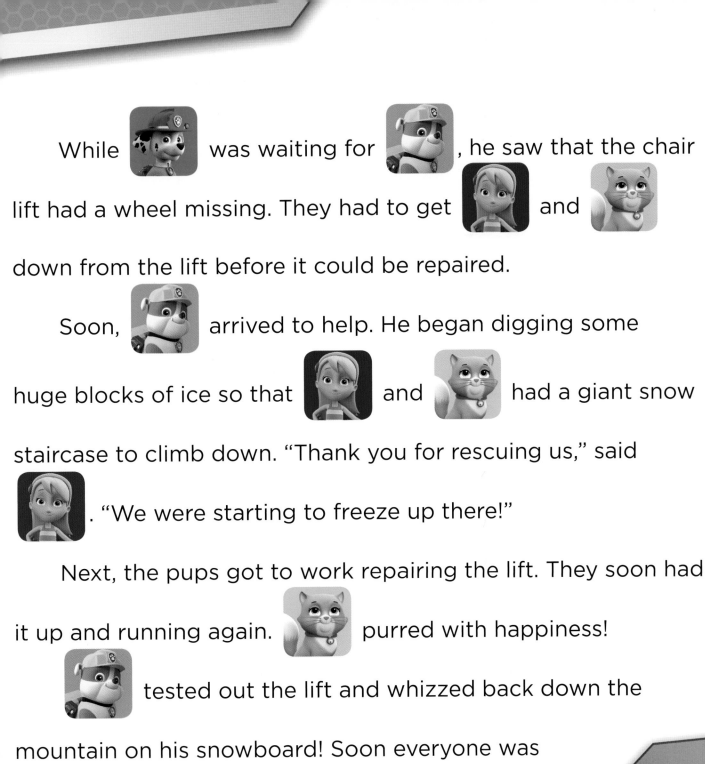 was waiting for , he saw that the chair lift had a wheel missing. They had to get and down from the lift before it could be repaired.

Soon, arrived to help. He began digging some huge blocks of ice so that and had a giant snow staircase to climb down. "Thank you for rescuing us," said . "We were starting to freeze up there!"

Next, the pups got to work repairing the lift. They soon had it up and running again. purred with happiness! tested out the lift and whizzed back down the mountain on his snowboard! Soon everyone was sliding and zooming down the slopes. What a pup-tacular day!

The End

Lots of SPOTS

Marshall has lost his famous Dalmatian spots. Can you draw them back for him? Colour them in in any shade you like!

Pup Fact

Marshall carries a first aid kit in his Pup Pack to help anyone in trouble.

Ready to ROLL!

Make way for Marshall, ready for another ruff-ruff rescue! Join the dots to finish the picture of Marshall's fire engine.

Pup Tag MATCH

The PAW Patrol pups wear their Pup Tags with pride! But which tag belongs to which pup? Draw lines to match the pairs.

The answers are on page 69.

Now draw your own Pup Tag that shows your favourite thing to do!

Pup, Pup, BOOGIE

Skye is playing her favourite game with her friends! Play some music to join in the Pup Pup Boogie! Roll a dice, then try the dance move for the number on which it lands.

You will need:

- A dice
- A large space, inside or out!
- Something that plays your favourite tunes.

1 Paws in the air!

Wave your 'paws' in the air like Rocky!

2 Roll over!

Get down on the floor and roll, roll, roll like Marshall!

3 Tail wag!

Move your hips from side to side.

4 Hop to it!

Stand on one leg and do the puppy hop!

5 Reach for the stars!

Stretch up high to catch a star.

6 Freestyle!

Perform any of the earlier moves or make up a move of your own!

Great Dancing!

Pup at PLAY

Hip, hip, hooray! Rocky's here to play! Colour in Rocky, then doodle a pattern on his kite.

Pup Fact

If something is broken, Rocky is the pup to fix it!

Recycle with ROCKY

Rocky is busy recycling, turning old rubbish into something new. Draw ticks when you find the four little pictures in the big one.

The answers are on page 69.

37

Help RYDER!

Ryder is playing a reading game. Will you help him? Say the words out loud.

pup

hat

jam

cat

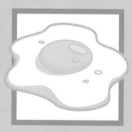

egg

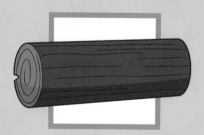

log

Now look for the words on Ryder's computer screen. They go forwards and down.

```
p h r e g g
j a m y s z
s t r h w u
p i f d g l
u c a t b o
p x e g m g
```

The answers are on page 69.

Ready, Set, GET WET!

Zuma the Chocolate Labrador is all about the water! Colour him in using the little picture to help you.

Pup Fact

Zuma can go underwater with his scuba diving gear on in his hovercraft.

DIVE IN!

Zuma is having a PAWsome time underwater! Count how many green fish and yellow fish there are, then write the numbers in the boxes.

The answers are on page 69.

Pups Find a Snow Monster

1. **I can't wait for Snow Day!**

2. **Bad news dude ...**

The pups were looking forward to Snow Day on Jake's Mountain. "I don't want to miss a minute!" said Rubble.

Jake called Ryder. "I've got bad news!" Jake said. "We have to cancel Adventure Bay Snow Day." Rubble's tail stopped wagging.

3. **A snow monster is on the loose!**

4. **GASP!**

"Everyone thinks that there's a snow monster!" said Jake. "We've spotted tracks and Alex even made a video of the beast."

Jake was worried about staying safe. "If we don't find the monster, we'll have to close the slopes for the winter, or maybe forever!" he sighed.

"The PAW Patrol will work out what's going on," Ryder told Jake. Rubble felt sad.

Don't worry, Rubble.

6

PAW Patrol, here's the plan.

7

zOOM!

At the Lookout, Ryder had a plan. "Chase, I need your nose and net to catch whatever's making those tracks," he said. "Rubble can bulldoze the snow."

Ryder, Chase and Rubble raced to Jake's Mountain in search of the monster. It wasn't long before they spotted tracks!

8

Suddenly, there was a huge roar! Rubble and Chase leapt into Ryder's arms. "There's no need to be scared of a little noise, pups," smiled Ryder.

9

Just then, Chase spotted the monster's nose behind Ryder! He tried to catch it, but trapped Ryder in his net instead! "Sorry!" called Chase.

10

Suddenly, from behind a tree, Bettina the cow, Garbie the goat and Chickaletta the chicken appeared – standing one on top of each other!

11

The tracks were made by some boots that Bettina found, together with Chickaletta's footprints! It wasn't a monster at all!

12

AAA-CHOO!

"Let's take the 'monster' back to show Jake," laughed Ryder. But just then, Chase let out a huge sneeze! "Aaa-choo!"

13

It's the animals making the noise!

Bettina, Garbie and Chickaletta ran away feeling scared – mooing, bleating and clucking loudly as they made their escape!

14

Well done, pups. You saved Snow Day!

Later on, Ryder explained the truth about the 'monster'. Farmer Yumi and Mayor Goodway came to collect their animals. Jake was happy – he could open the slopes again!

Good job, pups!

Snow PUP

Off the trail, Everest won't fail! Colour in Everest using the little picture to help you.

Pup Fact

Everest is the pup to call for any rescues in the snow.

What Comes NEXT?

Everest has a snowy mission for you! Which picture should come at the end of each row to complete the patterns?

1

2

3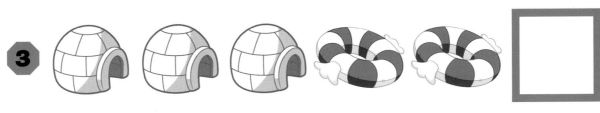

4

The answers are on page 69.

Adventure Bay FRIENDS

Besides Ryder and the PAW Patrol pups, there are lots of people to meet in Adventure Bay. How many friendly faces do you know?

Katie

Katie is Ryder's best friend. She helps animals to stay healthy and look their best at her Pet Parlour.

Did you know? Katie has a cute but cheeky cat called Cali.

Alex

Little Alex wants to be just like Ryder when he's bigger. He's always riding into trouble on his trike!

Did you know? Alex's grandfather is Mr Porter.

Farmer Yumi

This friendly farmer lives on Fuji Farm, in the hills of Adventure Bay. She grows fruit and vegetables and looks after all her farm animals there.

Did you know? Farmer Yumi is a martial arts master in Pup-Fu!

Cap'n Turbot

Cap'n Turbot is a fisherman. He spends most of his time out at sea, on his boat called the Flounder. He lives in the lighthouse on Seal Island.

Did you know?
Cap'n Turbot is named after a kind of fish!

Jake

Jake is a ranger who lives in a cabin on Jake's mountain. He comes to the rescue of anyone stuck in the snow, with the help of his snow pup, Everest.

Did you know?
Jake and Everest have been good friends since she rescued him at the South Pole.

Mayor Goodway

The mayor of Adventure Bay, Mayor Goodway lives at City Hall. She has a chicken called Chickaletta who lives in her handbag!

Did you know?
Mayor Goodway is afraid of heights.

Mr Porter

Mr Porter runs Porter's Market and a restaurant. He's kind, wise and caring, and loves his grandson Alex.

Did you know?
Poor Mr Porter was once sprayed by a stinky skunk!

Mayor Humdinger

Mayor Humdinger is the Mayor of Foggy Bottom, the town next to Adventure Bay. He's a little mean and is always causing trouble.

Did you know?
Mayor Humdinger does not like pups – especially the PAW Patrol.

A Very BUSY DAY

Ryder and the pups have had a busy day! Decide what time of day they did each thing. Was it in the morning, the afternoon or at night? Tick the box each time.

morning

afternoon

night

Be careful: you may need to tick more than one box!

1 Went on a morning rescue

2 Went to bed

50

3 Brushed their teeth

4 Had breakfast

5 Read a bedtime story

6 Got dressed

The answers are on page 69.

Pups Save the Treats

Read along with the story. Each time you get to a picture, say the name out loud.

Key:

| Mr Porter | Ryder | Chase | Zuma |

It was a cold and icy day. The PAW Patrol pups were standing

by to help anyone in trouble. was out making deliveries

in his van. His first stop was the Lookout, to drop off some pup

treats. But the icy road made the van's wheels slip and slide!

 drove on to the Lookout, very slowly. Suddenly, the

van started to slide down the hill towards the icy bay.

 called , and the PAW Patrol quickly gathered.

"We have to stop Mr Porter's van falling through the ice!"

told the pups. " , I'll need you to pull the van clear.

I'll ride with  on his hovercraft. We'll hook 's winch

to the van." The PAW Patrol was ruff-ruff ready!

 began to unwind his winch.  went to help,

but the ice started to crack under his feet! With no time to lose,

 quickly found a life buoy and pulled  safely aboard

the hovercraft. "Let's head for dry land, fast!" smiled .

Next,  towed the van back to safety.

Back at the Lookout, everyone was soon cosy and dry. "My

van is safe, all thanks to you," smiled . "And the pup treats

are safe too!" said .

"You pups really were great today," added .

"Maybe it's time for some of 's ..."

"Treats!" yelped the hungry pups.

What a day!

The End

Hear Me ROAR!

Rex is a good friend to the dinosaurs in Dino Wilds. Colour him in using your brightest colours!

Pup Fact

Rex gets around using a wheeled dino walker – nothing slows him down!

Jungle JUMBLE

Things are all mixed up in Dino Wilds today! Can you help Rex find three things in the picture that don't look quite right? Let's dino do this!

The answers are on page 69.

Dino Rescue GAME

It's time for a ruff-ruff rescue! Help Rex save his dino friends from the volcano lava!

How to play:

- Place your counters at the **START**.
- Take it in turns to throw the dice and move around the board.
- If you land on an orange space, follow the instructions.
- The winner is the player who reaches the **FINISH** first.
- The youngest player starts.

START

You will need:

A dice, and a counter for each player.

1

2

3

16

15

14
Take a shortcut to number 20.

17

18

19
Rocky clears the path. Move forwards 1 space.

20

6

7
The path is blocked! Throw a 6 to move on.

8

5

9

4
Rex is racing in his ROARsome vehicle. Zoom forwards 2 spaces.

10
A mighty T. rex roars you on 1 space!

11

13

12

FINISH

21

22

23
Stop to give a baby dino a lift. Miss a turn.

It's AUTUMN!

Rocky and Marshall love jumping in piles of autumn leaves! Find where each piece goes in the jigsaw picture.

a

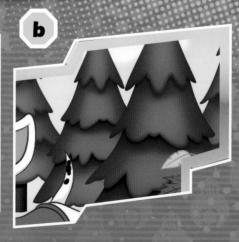

b

c

The answers are on page 69.

Hungry PUP

Draw a tasty treat in Rubble's bowl.
What do you think he would like to eat?

Make a Friendly OCTOPUS

Did you know that the PAW Patrol pups once saved a baby octopus and helped it to find its mother? Try this fun craft to make an octopus of your own!

You will need:

- a paper plate
- safety scissors
- tissue paper
- glue
- a ruler
- string
- sticky tape
- pens

Ask an adult to help you.

1

Ask an adult to cut the plate in half.

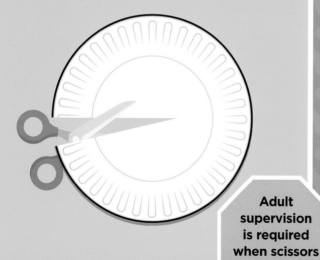

Adult supervision is required when scissors are in use.

2

Cut a piece of tissue paper that's big enough to cover the semi-circle plate.

3

Glue the tissue paper to the front of the plate, sticking any extra tissue paper to the back of the plate.

4

Cut some long strips of tissue paper, about 5 cm wide and 20 cm long. Then stick them to the bottom (straight) edge of the plate. These will be the tentacles!

5

When the glue has dried, turn the plate over and stick a loop of string to the top using your tape.

You could add more decorations to your octopus if you like!

6

Draw two eyes and a mouth and your octopus is finished. Hang it up for everyone to see!

Bang the DRUM!

Musical Everest loves to make some noise on the drums! Spot six things that are different in the second picture.

Colour in a star for each difference you find.

The answers are on page 69.

Ryder's MEMORY GAME

Ryder has taken a photo of the pups on his PupPad. Look closely at the picture below for one whole minute, then answer the questions on the next page.

What can you remember?
Read the sentences, then
decide whether each one
is true or false.

1 There are five pups in the picture.

true ☑ false ☑

2 Chase is at the top of the tower.

true ☑ false ☑

3 The pups are wearing their uniforms.

true ☑ false ☑

4 One pup is fast asleep.

true ☑ false ☑

5 There is only one girl pup.

true ☑ false ☑

Turn to the answers on page 69 to see how many questions you got right!

Mountain MAZE

Jake's Mountain is the perfect spot for some snowboarding! Which path should the pups take to reach Jake's cabin at the bottom of the mountain?

START

FINISH

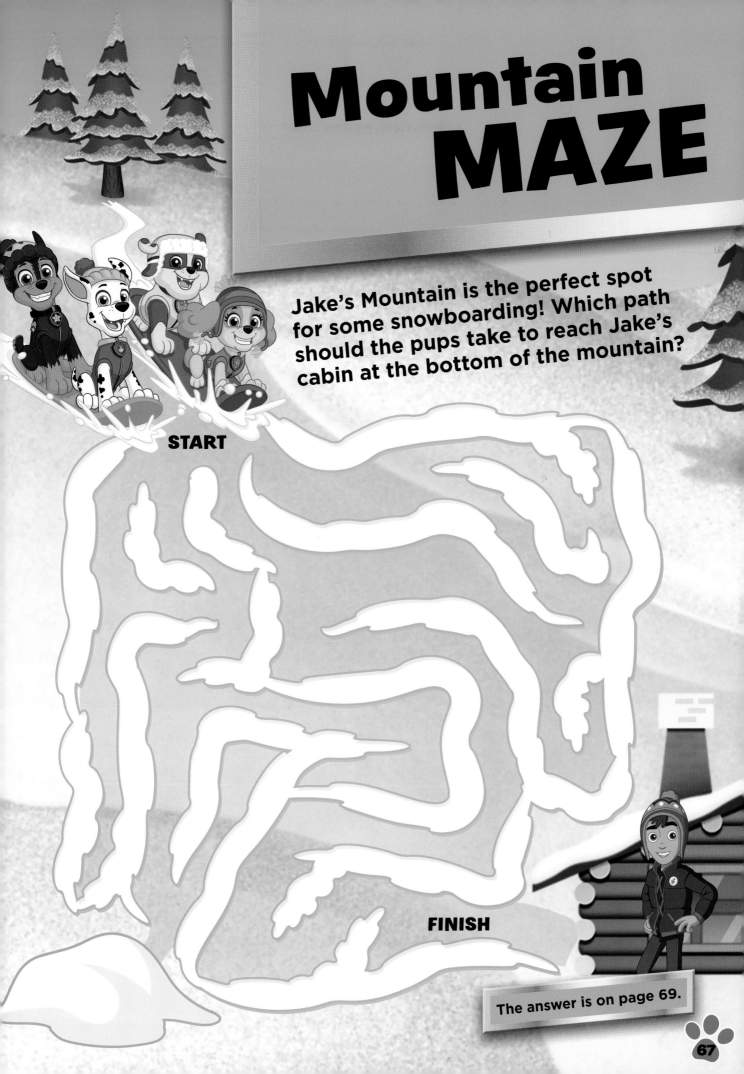

The answer is on page 69.

Around the TREE

The pups can't wait for Christmas! Help them count how many of each festive item there is in the picture.

The answers are on page 69.

68

Answers

Pages 8-9
Ready for Action!

Page 11   On the Case!
Shadow d matches Chase.

Page 13   Perfect Pets
Chickaletta belongs to Mayor Goodway. Bettina belongs to Farmer Yumi. Cali belongs to Katie. Ryder doesn't have a pet.

Page 19   Take a Break
a and e are the matching pictures.

Pages 20-21   Guess Who?
1. Skye; 2. Chase; 3. Everest; 4. Rubble; 5. Rocky; 6. Zuma.

Page 23
This Pup's Gotta Fly!
The penguin can't fly.

Pages 24-25   Party Pups!

Pages 26-27   On the Road

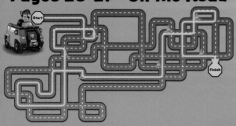

Pages 32-33 Pup Tag Match

Page 37 Recycle with Rocky

Pages 38-39   Help Ryder!

Page 41   Dive In!

Page 47
What Comes Next?

Pages 50-51
A Very Busy Day
1. morning; 2. night; 3. morning & night; 4. morning; 5. night; 6. morning.

Page 55   Jungle Jumble

Page 58   It's Autumn!

Page 62   Bang the Drum

Pages 65-66
Ryder's Memory Game
1. true; 2. false – it was Skye; 3. true; 4. false – the pups were all awake; 5. false – Skye and Everest are girl pups.

Page 67
Mountain Maze

Page 68   Around the Tree